Student Response Book

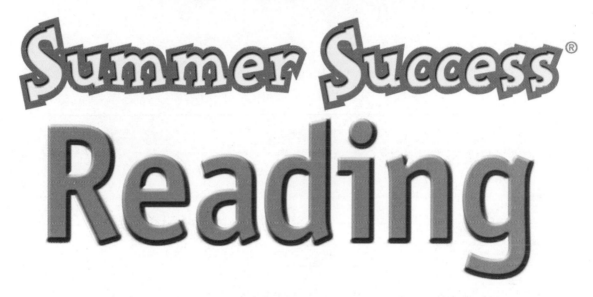

Summer Success®
Reading

James F. Baumann • Michael F. Opitz • Laura Robb

GReaT SouRCe®
EDUCATION GROUP
A Houghton Mifflin Company

Credits

Writer: Susan Ring

Manager/Editor: Ellen Sternhell

Design/Production: Jim Bartosik/Andy Cox, Ed Pokorski

Illustration: Chris Vallo and Jim Higgins

Poetry: "No Drip of Rain" by Ivy O. Eastwick. Copyright by the author. "The Crocodile's Dentist" from *Moon Frog.* Text © 1992 Richard Edwards. Reproduced by permission of Candlewick Press Inc., Cambridge, Massachusetts, on behalf of Walker Books Ltd., London. "Taste of Purple" by Leland B. Jacobs. From *Is Somewhere Always Far Away?* by Leland B. Jacobs. Text copyright, © 1967 by Leland B. Jacobs. Reprinted by permission of Henry Holt and Company, LLC. "Ants" from *Yellow Butter Purple Jelly Red Jam Black Bread* by Mary Ann Hoberman. Copyright © 1981 by Mary Ann Hoberman. "Dickery Dean" by Dennis Lee. From *Jelly Belly* (Macmillan of Canada, 1983). Copyright © 1983 Dennis Lee. With permission of the author.

Printed in the United States of America

International Standard Book Number: 0-669-48523-3

2 3 4 5 6 7 8 9 10 - MZ - 07 06 05 04 03 02

Questions Good Readers Ask Themselves

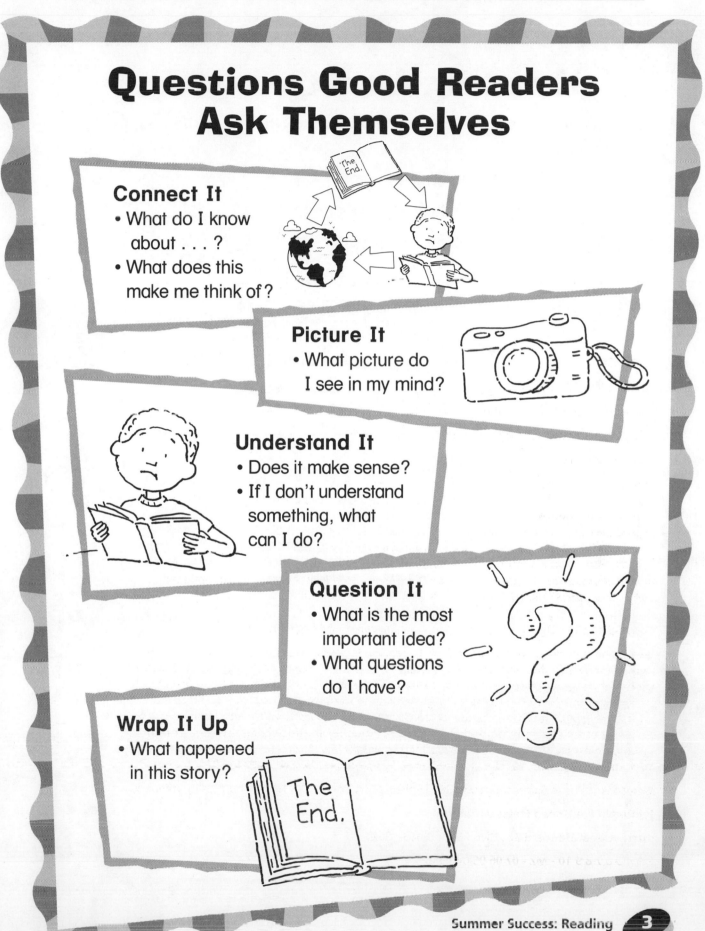

Connect It
- What do I know about . . . ?
- What does this make me think of?

Picture It
- What picture do I see in my mind?

Understand It
- Does it make sense?
- If I don't understand something, what can I do?

Question It
- What is the most important idea?
- What questions do I have?

Wrap It Up
- What happened in this story?

Reading Log Questions

Choose one question to answer for each book that you write about in the Reading Log.

1 What did this book remind you of?

2 What did you learn that was new or interesting?

3 What was this book mainly about?

4 What questions do you have for the author?

5 How is the main character like you?

READING LOG

Title _____

Question # _____

_____

_____

_____

Title _____

Question # _____

_____

_____

_____

READING LOG

Title _____

Question # _____

_____

_____

_____

_____

Title _____

Question # _____

_____

_____

_____

_____

Title _____

Question # _____

_____

_____

_____

_____

READING LOG

Title _____

Question # _____

_____

_____

_____

_____

Title _____

Question # _____

_____

_____

_____

_____

Title _____

Question # _____

_____

_____

_____

_____

Things Good Readers Do to Read Words

Look at the whole word
- Look at the beginning of the word.
- Look at the middle of the word.
- Look at the end of the word.

c a t

Look at parts of the word
- Look for parts of the word that you know.

c a t

Look at the whole page
- Think what would make sense.
- Look at the pictures.

This is a cat.

Word Bank

Week 1

_____
_____
_____
_____

Week 2

_____
_____
_____
_____

Week 3

_____
_____
_____
_____

Week 4

_____
_____
_____
_____

Week 5

_____
_____
_____
_____

Week 6

_____
_____
_____
_____

Reading Strategies Survey

1 **Before I read a book, I usually do these things:**

(Check any of the following strategies that you do.)

_____ ask someone what it's about

_____ look at the pictures

_____ look to see whether it's too hard

_____ look to see whether it's too easy

_____ guess what it's about

_____ read the back cover or the jacket flap

2 **When I'm reading and I don't understand what's happening, I usually try to** _____

_____ .

3 **When I get stuck on a word, I usually** _____ ,

or I might _____ .

(Check any of the following strategies that you do.)

_____ ask someone

_____ skip it and read on

_____ read the whole part again

_____ try to sound it out

_____ look it up

_____ think of a word that makes sense

4 **After I finish a book I liked a lot, I usually** _____ .

(Check any of the following strategies that you do.)

_____ talk to a friend about it

_____ take a rest from reading

_____ look for another book by the same author

_____ choose a new book

_____ read the book again

_____ draw or write about it

_____ think of how it was like my life

_____ ask someone to suggest another book

Name _____ Date _____

Reading Interest Survey

Put a ✔ in the spaces to show your answers.

1 Do you like to read?

____ yes   ____ sometimes   ____ no

2 What kinds of books do you like to read?
Mark all the ones you like.

____ animal   ____ poems

____ adventure   ____ riddles/jokes

____ folktales   ____ about people

____ funny   ____ series

3 What is your favorite book? _____

_____

4 Who is your favorite author? _____

_____

5 What magazines do you like to read? _____

_____

6 When and where do you read? _____

_____

7 How do you choose books to read? _____

_____

Dear Parent or Caregiver,

This summer, your child will be using the **Summer Success: Reading** program. This program will provide instruction in reading skills and strategies to help your child read better. **Summer Success: Reading** features different types of reading (fiction, nonfiction, poetry) and topics. Each week, your child will bring home a weekly newsletter so you will be able to keep in touch with your child's activities in summer school.

Summer Success: Reading emphasizes reading strategies. This means that the program has instruction in helping your child understand what he or she is reading. One example of a strategy is "making connections." A reader who makes connections asks questions like "What do I know about this?" "What does this remind me of?" "How am I like this character?" When a reader can make connections, she or he understands the text.

Summer Success: Reading also works with words, helping your child become better at reading and writing words. A section of the lesson called Read & Explore Words focuses on how words work. Children will study words, make words from letters, classify words, and—in general—get to know words.

But we cannot do it alone at school. We need your help as well. On the back of this letter are things you can do at home to support the summer school program. Doing reading and writing activities every day will help your child develop her or his reading ability this summer and beyond. Please let me know if you have any questions. Thank you.

Educationally yours,

Your child's teacher

Read, Read, Read!

The more you read with your child, the more opportunities he or she will have to enjoy reading and improve reading skills. Try to have a variety of books at home. If you don't know what books to get, ask other children what they like to read. Librarians, bookstore workers, and teachers are good resources, too.

Make sure your child reads every day.

- Read aloud to your child.
- Take turns with your child reading paragraphs or pages.
- As you read together, ask your child what he or she thinks. Share your thoughts, too.

Model how to think about the text. Say things like,

"This reminds me of —"

"I wonder why —"

"I predict that —"

"I would like to ask the author—"

When your child has free time, try one of these ideas.

- Read a book.
- Read a magazine or newspaper.
- Read a recipe and cook something.
- Make up a play with a friend.
- Write your own story.

Name _____ Date _____

No Drip of Rain

by Ivy O. Eastwick

It rained on Anne,

it rained on Fan,

it rained on Arabella,

but—

it did not rain

on Mary Jane —

SHE had a HUGE umbrella.

Draw a picture of yourself holding an umbrella.

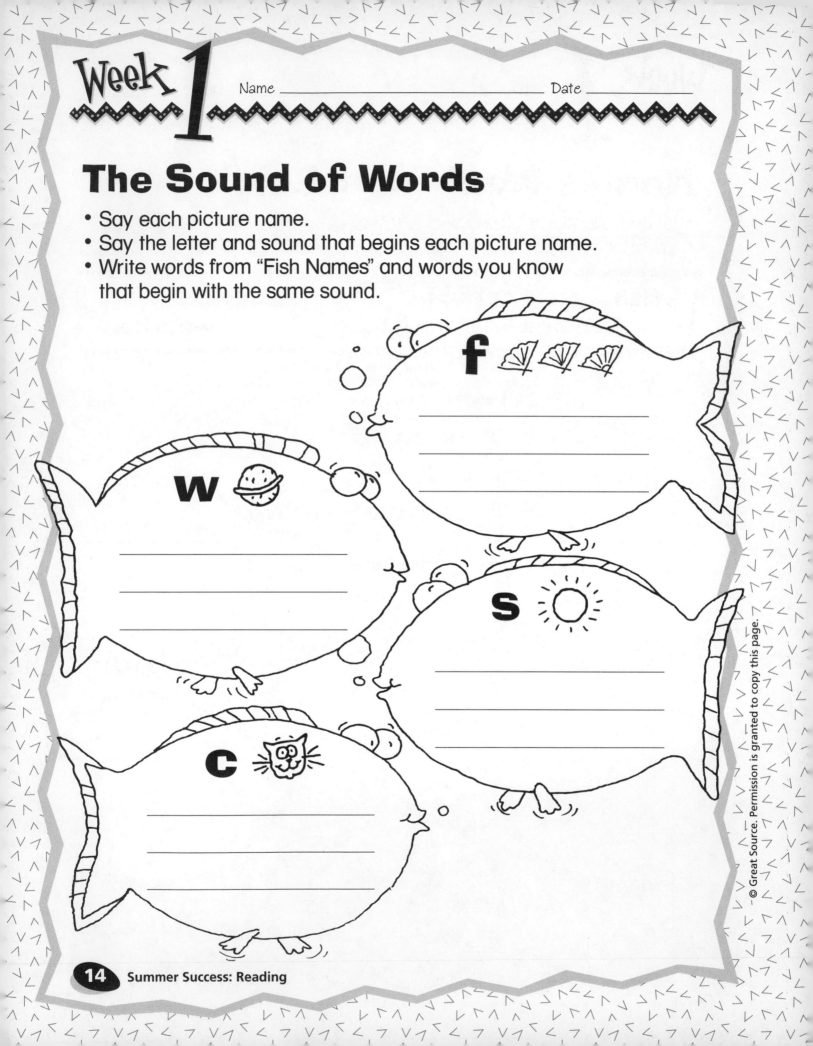

The Sound of Words

- Say each picture name.
- Say the letter and sound that begins each picture name.
- Write words from "Fish Names" and words you know that begin with the same sound.

Names Web

- Write a word from the box in each circle.
- Write or draw something in each circle about the word.

fish	people	colors
things	animals	weather

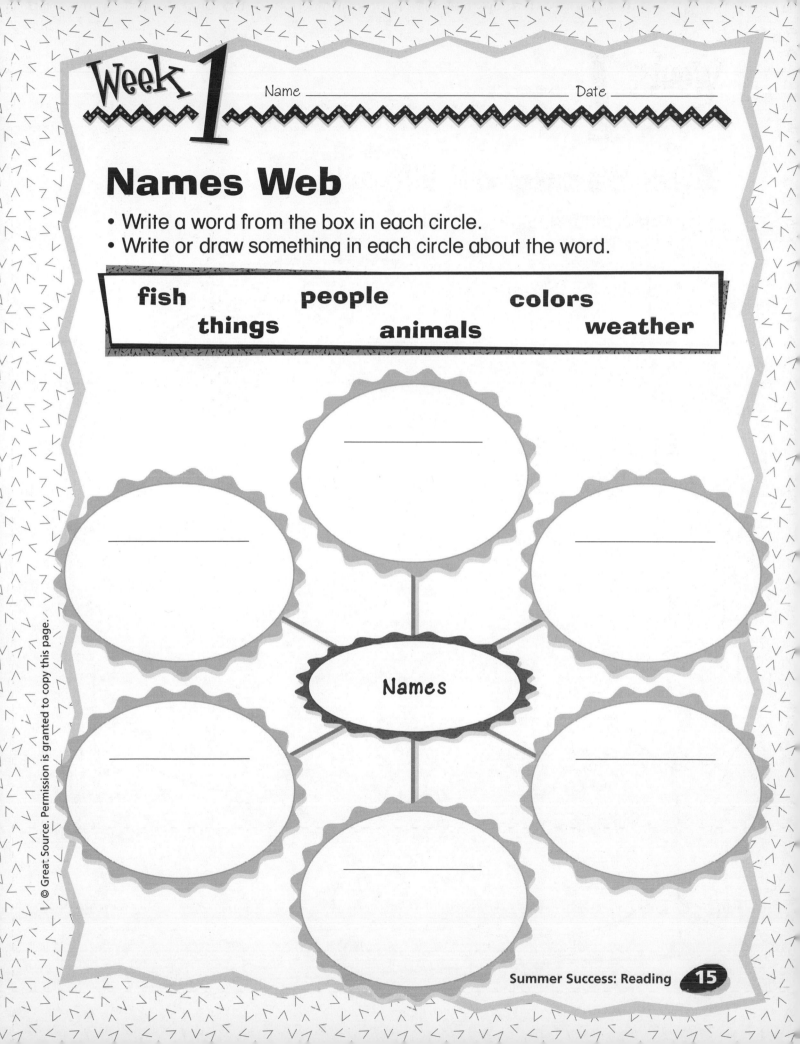

A Pet I Want

• Draw and write about a pet you want.

Dear Diary,

This is the pet I want.

This pet is a _____

My pet can _____

I will name my pet _____

Love,

_____
(your name)

Words to Name People and Things

- Read each sentence.
- Finish the last one.
- Draw a picture to go with each sentence.

1 **Bill holds a bill.**

2 **Ruby wears a ruby ring.**

3 **Jay sees a blue jay.**

4 **Pearl wears a _____ .**

Word Fun

- Make words from the letters in the word **NAMES**.
- Write the words on the chart.
- You get one point for each word you make.

names

a

_____

_____

_____

m

_____

_____

_____

_____

_____

s

_____

_____

I got _____ points!

Story Map

- What happened in the story "How Snake Got Its Name"?
- Fill in the story map with words and pictures.
- Retell the story!

How Snake Got Its Name

First,

_____

_____

Next,

_____

_____

Then,

_____

_____

_____

Last,

_____

_____

Your Own Story

- Plan a story about why an animal makes its sound.
- Draw your story plans in the boxes.
- Write your story on another sheet of paper.

tweet

1 Draw the animal and write its name.

squeak

2 Draw and write the sound it used to make.

MEOW

3 Draw what changes the animal's sound.

arf

4 Draw and write the sound the animal makes now.

oink

Name _____ Date _____

Make Rhymes

- Write a word to make a rhyme.
- Read the rhymes to a friend.

1 See the big frog.

It sits on a _____.

2 You can smell a rose.

Just use your _____.

3 I like this shell

that is shaped like a _____.

4 This bee has wings.

Sometimes it _____!

Name _____ Date _____

Self-Evaluation

1 One new thing I tried this week is _____

_____

_____

_____

2 Two new words I learned to read this week are

_____

_____

3 Two new words I learned to write this week are

_____

_____

4 My favorite story or book this week is _____

_____

5 Next week I want to _____

_____

_____

_____

Did you name my pets?

They are Ben, Mike, Sue, and Trish.

8

My Pets' Names

1

My pets and I play games.

But sometimes I forget their names!

Hmmmm

6

My cat's name is Mike.

He rides a little bike.

3

My dog's name is Ben.

He looks at TV in the den.

2

Do you remember my pets' names?

See how many names you can remember.

Say the names.

7

My rabbit's name is Sue.

She hides inside my shoe.

4

My turtle's name is Trish.

She likes to sit in a dish.

5

Week 1 Newsletter

This week we have been reading about names. We have read a book, some magazine articles, and some poems. Ask your child to tell you about the book that was read aloud and the *Names* magazine.

The word of the week was *names*. Together, the class listed names of people, places, and things. On another day, the class used the letters in *names* to make words. Then, the words were grouped by what they had in common—the same beginning sound, the same number of letters, and so on.

Here's what your child has to say about the week:

_____

_____

_____

_____

_____

_____

_____

_____

_____

_____

_____

You, Your Child, and Reading

There are many sources to help you find good books to read with your child. Since fresh ideas are always helpful, here are some books that you might read with your child.

***Christopher Changes His Name* by Itah Sadu (Firefly, 1998)**
Christopher is tired of having such an ordinary name, and so he wants to change it, until he realizes that he's special just the way he is. The family portrayed in this book is from Trinidad.

***From Anne to Zach* by Mary Jane Martin (Boyds Mill, 1996)**
Using simple, repetitive language, the letters of the alphabet are reviewed while introducing different children and their names.

***Hello, Biscuit* by Alyssa Capucilli (Greenwillow, 1998)**
Biscuit is a puppy who stars in a series of beginning readers. In this first installment, Biscuit arrives and is named by his new family.

***How I Named the Baby* by Linda Shute (Whitman, 1993)**
James helps his family name his new baby sister. They go through a long list of names—and their meanings—but when the baby arrives in the month of June, the right choice is obvious.

***Josephina Hates Her Name* by Diana Engel (Consortium, 1999)**
Josephina doesn't like her name until she learns that she is named after her grandmother's talented and daring sister. Read aloud.

***Naming the Cat* by Laurence P. Pringle (Walker, 1999)**
When a family adopts a stray cat, they're not sure what to call it. As they debate the question, the cat's brushes with disaster make it clear that its name should be "Lucky."

***Tikki Tikki Tembo* retold by Arlene Mosel (Scholastic, 1988)**
A long time ago, a boy in China had an impossibly long name that began Tikki Tikki Tembo, but his brother was simply called Chang. This folktale explains why Chinese people now give all children short names instead of great long names.

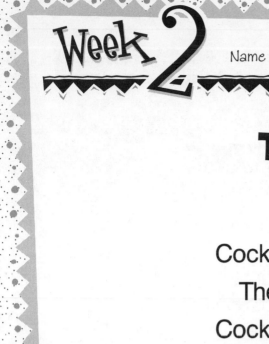

Name _____   Date _____

The Rooster

by Anonymous

Cock-a-doodle-doo!
   The rooster flaps his wings.
Cock-a-doodle-doo!
   He flaps his wings and sings.
Cock-a-doodle-doo!
   The rooster sings, and then
Cock-a-doodle!
Cock-a-doodle!
   He flaps his wings again.

 Write two words that rhyme with <u>wings</u>.

_____   _____

2 Draw a picture to go with the poem.

What Can Be on a Farm?

- Write the words from the box in the chart.
- Use your own words, too.

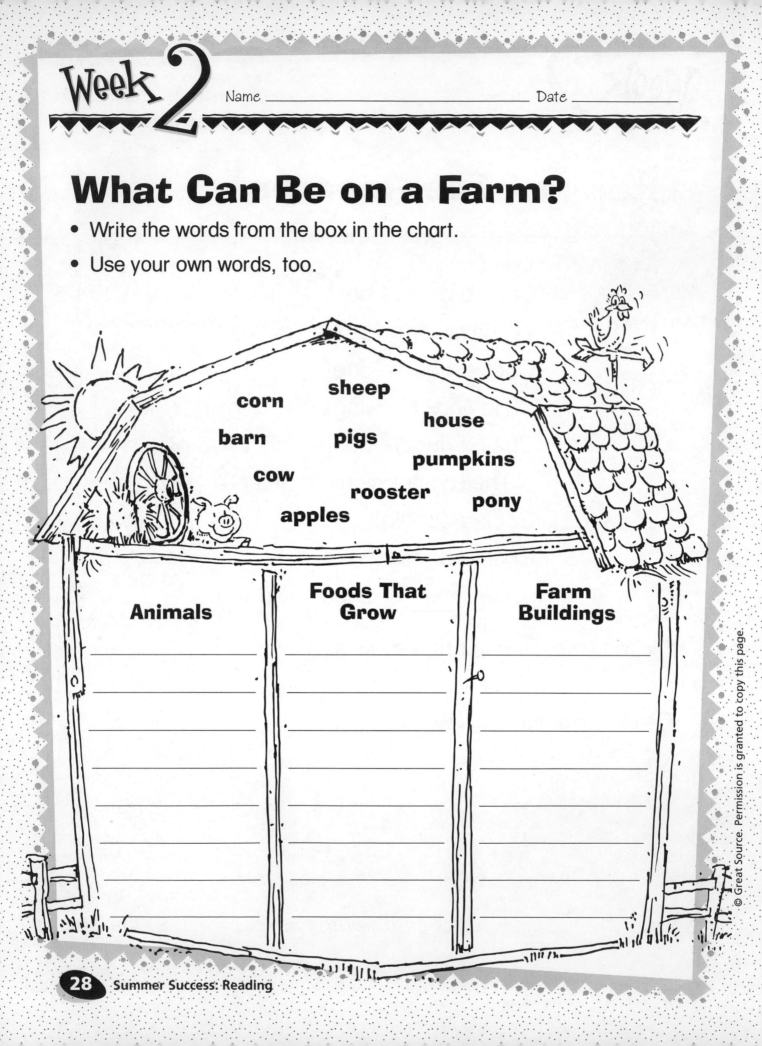

corn sheep house barn pigs cow pumpkins rooster pony apples

Animals	Foods That Grow	Farm Buildings

Name _____ Date _____

Steps to Get Popcorn

- Tell how we get popcorn.
- Fill in the missing word in each line.
- Use a word from the box.

| heat | | eat |
| pick | | buy |

1

We _____ the corn.

2

We _____ the corn.

3

We _____ the corn.

4

We _____ the corn.

Cows Give Milk

- Read each sentence.
- Finish the last sentence. Draw a picture for it.

1 This is a cow.

2 She lives on the farm.

3 The cow gives me something good.

4 The cow gives me _____

_____

Name _____   Date _____

Fun with Words

- Make words from the letters in the word **FARMER**.

- Write your words on the chart.

- You get one point for each word you make.

I got _____ points!

My Visit to a Farm

• Make believe you went to one of the farms in the <u>Found on Farms</u> magazine.

• Draw and write about the farm.

I went to a farm. This is what I saw.

I saw _____

_____

_____

_____

My Pony

- What if you had your own pony?
- Write a letter to a friend about your pony.
- Draw a picture to go with the letter.

Dear _____,

I have a pony.

The name of my pony is _____.

I feed my pony _____.

This is a picture of me riding my pony.

Love,

_____

Name _____ Date _____

Story Map

- What happened in "A Pig Named Sue"?
- Fill in the story map.
- Retell the story to a friend.

A Pig Named Sue

First,

_____

Next,

_____

Then,

_____

Last,

_____

Reading Chart

Fill in the chart.

Found on Farms Magazine	What I Remember
All Kinds of Corn	
How Do We Make Popcorn?	
Two Kinds of Farms	
On Grammy's Farm	
A Pig Named Sue	

Self-Evaluation

1 One new thing I tried this week is _____

_____

_____

_____

2 Two new words I learned to read this week are

_____   _____

3 Two new words I learned to write this week are

_____   _____

4 My favorite story or book this week is _____

_____

5 Next week I want to _____

_____

_____

_____

Take It Home!

8

Directions: Write your own story to go with the pictures. 1

6

3

2

7

4

5

Week 2 Newsletter

This week we have been reading about farms. We read a book, some magazine articles, and some poems. Ask your child to tell you about the book that was read aloud and the *Found on Farms* magazine.

The word of the week was *farmer*. Together, the class listed words that they think of when they hear the word *farmer*. On another day, the class used the letters in *farmer* to make smaller words (for example, *far, arm, farm*). Then, the words were grouped by what they had in common—rhyme, the same number of letters, and so on.

Here's what your child has to say about the week:

_____

_____

_____

_____

_____

_____

_____

_____

_____

_____

Word Games

Games are a great way to focus on words and their spellings. No one said learning has to be boring!

Letter by Letter

Can you think of something on a farm for each letter?

See how many you can think of from A to Z.

Take turns with someone else, going from letter to letter.

a	n
b	o
c	p
d	q
e	r
f	s
g	t
h	u
i	v
j	w
k	x
l	y
m	z

"The Crocodile's Dentist"

by Richard Edwards

Here is his mirror, here is his drill,

Here is his briefcase, here is his bill,

Here are his boots on the riverbank, so

Where did the crocodile's dentist go?

Picture It

Draw pictures of what you read. Then write about your pictures.

My Pictures	All About My Pictures

My Toothbrush

Let me tell you about my toothbrush. My toothbrush is

_____

_____

I use my toothbrush _____

_____

_____

If I do not use my toothbrush, _____

_____

_____

This is what my toothbrush looks like.

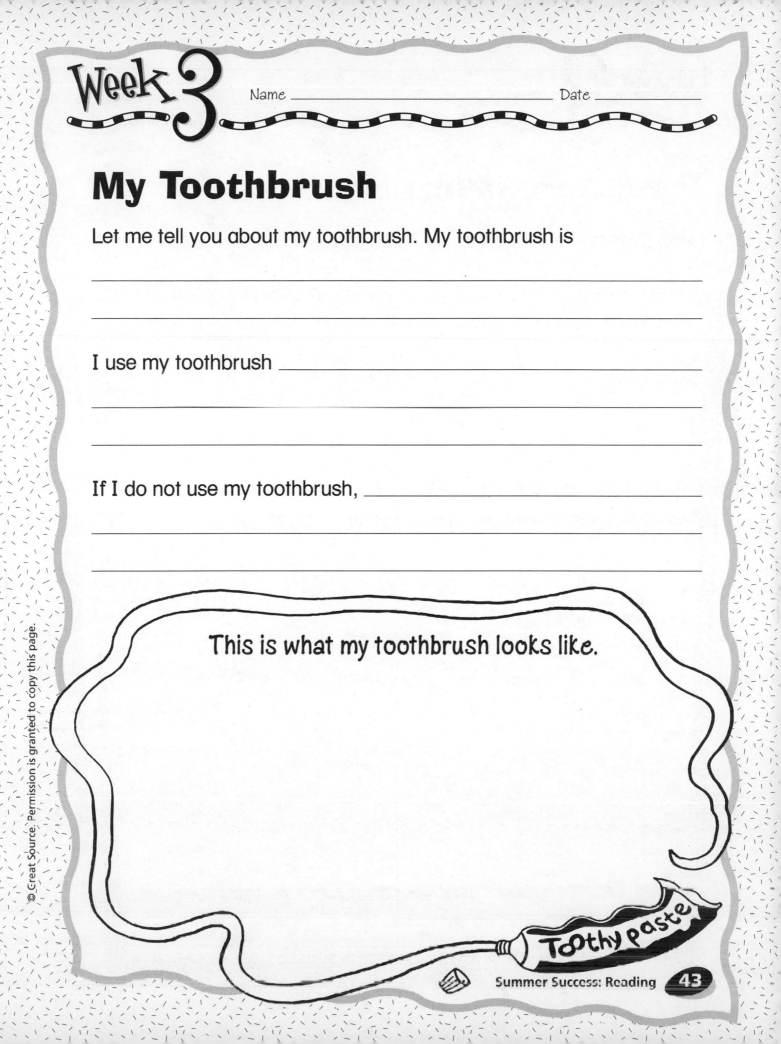

Plan a Poster

Write a title for your poster.

_____

Write three things you plan to put on your poster.

1 _____

2 _____

3 _____

Draw one of the pictures for your poster.

[drawing box]

Now make your poster on page 45.

Week 3

Name _____ Date _____

How Elephants Got Tusks

Retell the play. Write four things that happened in the play.

First, _____

_____

_____

_____

Next, _____

_____

_____

_____

Then, _____

_____

_____

_____

At the end, _____

_____

_____

_____

Make New Words

Look at each word. Take off the first letter. Put on a new letter.
What word do you have?

1

hot

cot _____

_____

_____

2

hop

_____

_____

3

hog

_____

_____

4

hoot

_____

_____

_____

Planning to Write

Make a writing plan. Draw or write your answers to these questions.

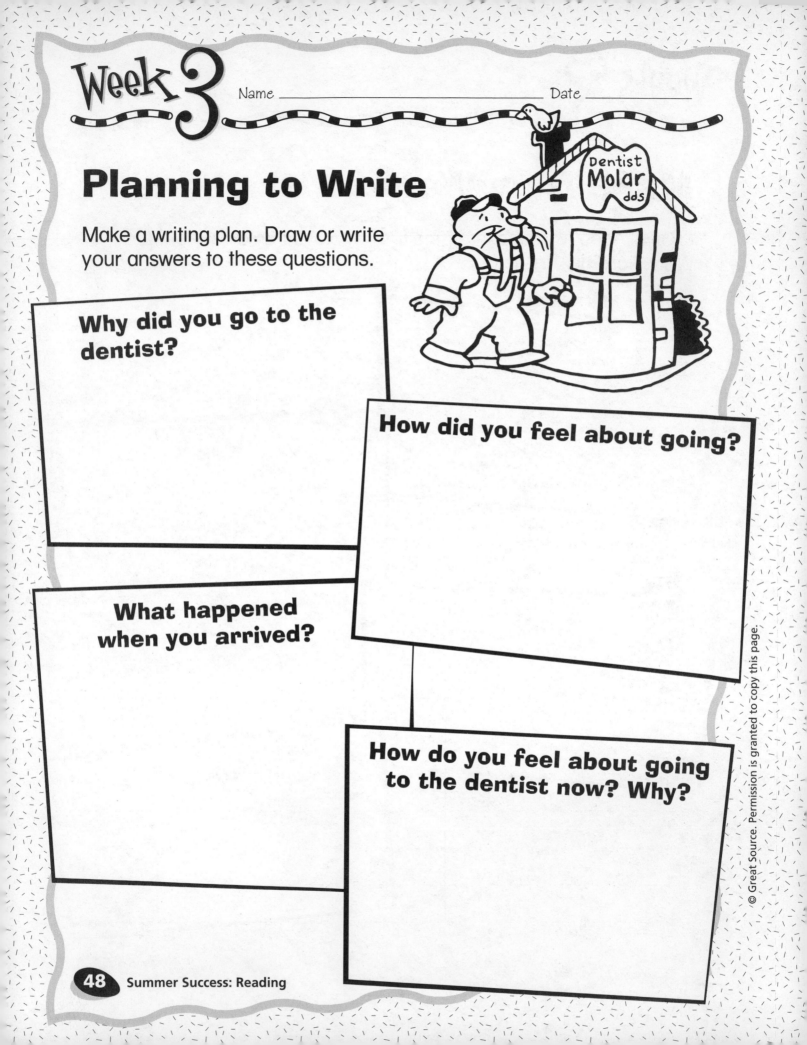

Why did you go to the dentist?

How did you feel about going?

What happened when you arrived?

How do you feel about going to the dentist now? Why?

My Trip to the Dentist

Write about your trip to the dentist. Use your notes on page 48.
Draw a picture.

_____

_____

_____

_____

_____

_____

_____

Self-Evaluation

1 One new strategy I tried this week is _____

_____

_____

_____

_____

2 Two new words I learned to read this week are

_____

_____

3 Two new words I learned to write this week are

_____

_____

4 My favorite story or book this week is _____

_____

5 My goal for next week is _____

_____

_____

_____

_____

1

Fold along gray line.

What I Learned About Teeth

This week I learned a lot about teeth.

I learned that there are different kinds of teeth.

Some teeth are big.

Some teeth are little.

I earned about dinosaur teeth.

Dinosaurs with flat teeth ate plants.

Dinosaurs with sharp teeth ate meat.

I learned a lot about teeth!

4

2

I learned how to take care of teeth.

I should brush my teeth morning and night.

I should go to the dentist, too.

I learned that elephants have tusks.

Some animals have very big teeth.

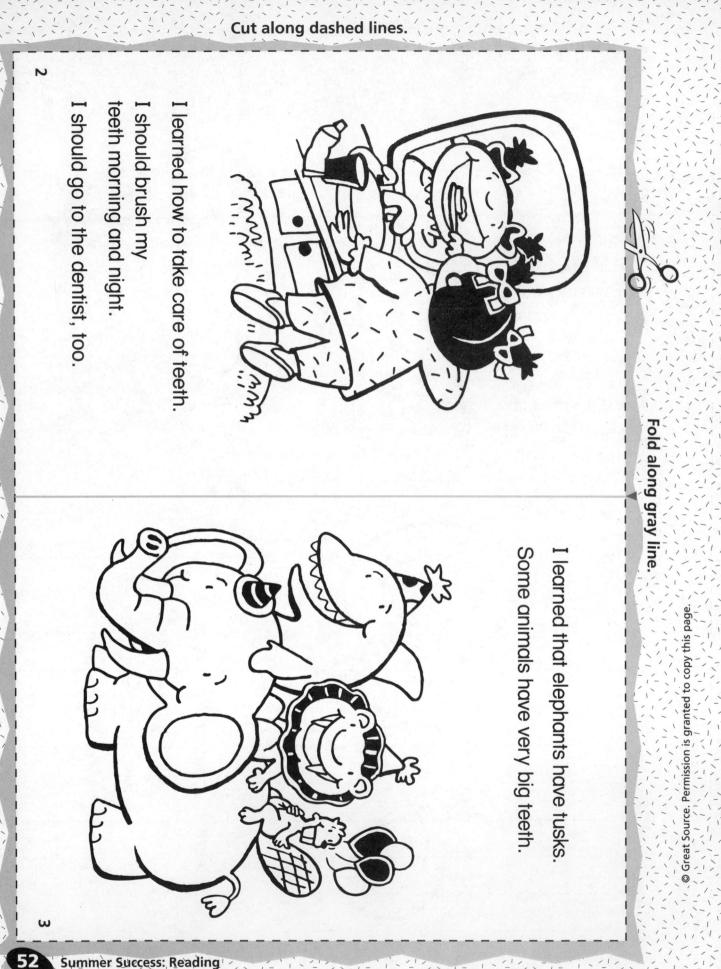

3

Week 3 Newsletter

This week we have been reading about teeth. We read a book and some magazine articles. Ask your child to tell you about the book that was read aloud and the *Teeth* magazine. We learned a poem together and read a play.

The word of the week was *toothbrush*. Together, the class listed words that they think of when they hear the word *toothbrush*. On another day, the class used the letters in *toothbrush* to make words. Here are the words we made: *or, to, so, us, hot, tot, rot, rob, rub, tub, shot, boot, hoot, hoots, shoot*. Then, we grouped the words. We made groups of words that have 2, 3, 4, or 5 letters. We also grouped words that rhyme.

Here's what your child has to say about the week:

_____

_____

_____

_____

_____

_____

_____

_____

_____

_____

Reading at Home

The best way to become better at reading is to read. Here are some more books about teeth that you and your child might enjoy reading together.

***Arthur's Loose Tooth* by Lillian Hoban (HarperTrophy, 1987)**
Arthur the Chimp learns a lesson about bravery when he has to confront his fear of losing a loose tooth.

***Arthur Tricks the Tooth Fairy* by Marc Brown (Random House, 1997)**
Arthur's sister is fascinated by the tooth fairy, and so she tries to pull out one of her teeth. Arthur comes to the rescue, saving her teeth and her belief in the tooth fairy.

***The Bear's Toothache* by David McPhail (Little, Brown, 1988)**
A boy takes the role of dentist and examines a bear with a toothache. The rotten tooth has to come out, so the boy uses whatever "tools" he has on hand.

***The Crocodile and the Dentist* by Taro Gomi (Millbrook, 1994)**
It's time for Crocodile to visit the dentist. Both he and the dentist are afraid of each other and dread the appointment. During the visit, they both think and say exactly the same things.

***A Look at Teeth* by Allan Fowler (Children's Press, 1988)**
An informative introduction to the function and anatomy of teeth in humans and other animals. With photos.

Name _____ Date _____

Taste of Purple

by Leland B. Jacobs

Grapes hang purple

In their bunches,

Ready for

September lunches.

Gather them, no

Minutes wasting.

Purple is

Delicious tasting.

Draw something purple. Write about your picture.

_____

_____

My Favorite Color

Write about your favorite color.

1 My favorite color is _____

2 I like it because _____

_____

3 The colors in my room are _____

_____

This is a picture of my room.

Colors in Our World

- Fill in the web to show where we see colors.
- Use words from the box.
- Then color the pictures!

on a street
on a map
in a rainbow
on a team

NEIGHBORHOOD MAP

Color is everywhere.

Your Own Story

- Plan a story about a tree that changes colors.
- Draw your story plans in the boxes.
- Write your story on another sheet of paper.

1 What kind of tree is in your story?

2 What happens first?

3 What happens next?

4 How does the story end?

Word Fun

- Make words from the letters in the word <u>rainbow</u>.
- Write the words on the chart.
- You get one point for each word you make.

Words with 2 letters	Words with 3 letters	Words with 4 letters	Words with 5 letters
_____	_____	_____	_____
_____	_____	_____	
_____	_____	_____	
	_____	_____	
	_____		
	_____		

I got _____ points!

What Do You Think?

- Read the sentences.
- Put a ✓ in the Yes box if the answer is yes.
- Put a ✓ in the No box if the answer is no.

Animals are only one color. ⬜ **Yes** ⬜ **No**

Colors help animals hide
from other animals. ⬜ **Yes** ⬜ **No**

Some animals can
change colors. ⬜ **Yes** ⬜ **No**

Colors help animals
find each other. ⬜ **Yes** ⬜ **No**

Write what you learned about how color helps animals.

_____

_____

_____

_____

_____

Mixing Colors

- Color each circle.
- What new colors have you made?

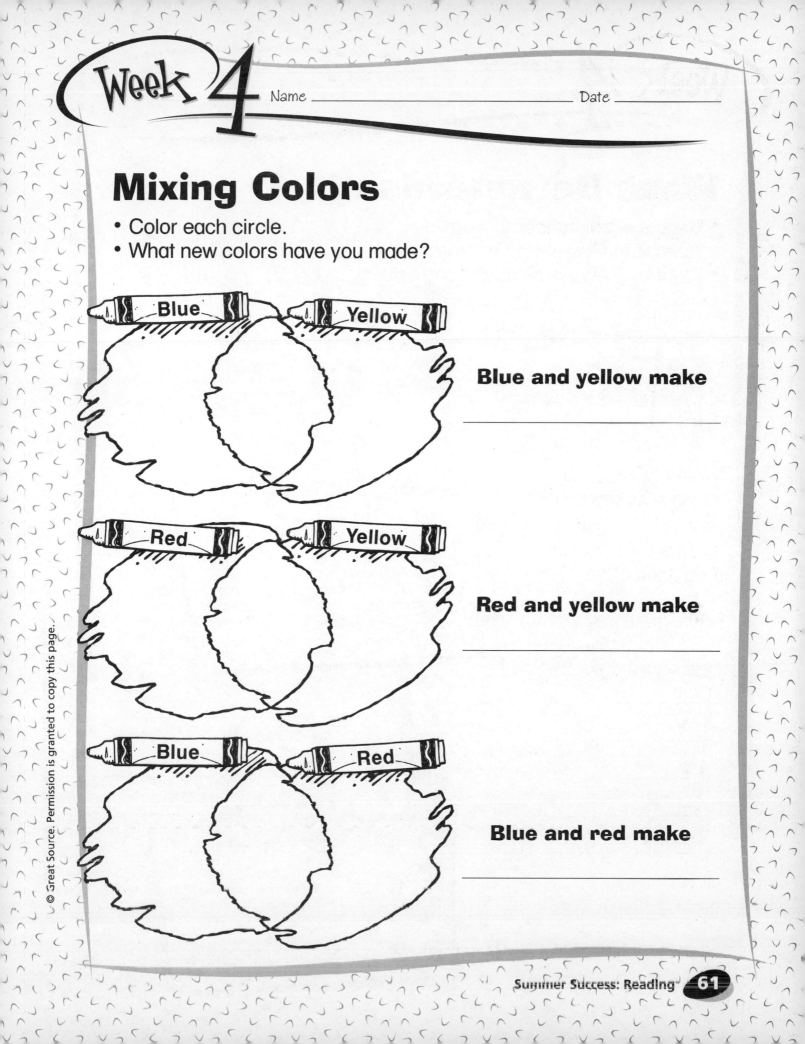

Blue   Yellow

Blue and yellow make

_____

Red   Yellow

Red and yellow make

_____

Blue   Red

Blue and red make

_____

Make New Words

- Look at each numbered word.
- Take off the first letter. Add the letter you see next to each line.
- Write the new words.

1 ran

t _____

c _____

m _____

2 win

p _____

t _____

f _____

3 bet

w _____

p _____

l _____

4 cat

h _____

m _____

b _____

Make Rhymes

- Write a word to make a rhyme.
- Read the rhymes to a friend.

Watch the rabbit go!

It hides in the cold, white _____ .

The squirrel is brown.

It will not come _____ .

Can you find the bug?

It's under the blue _____ .

The green light means go.

The yellow means _____ .

Self-Evaluation

1 One new thing I tried this week is _____

_____

2 Two new words I learned to read this week are

_____

_____

3 Two new words I learned to write this week are

_____

_____

4 My favorite story or book this week is

_____

5 Next week I want to _____

_____

_____

_____

You pick a color!

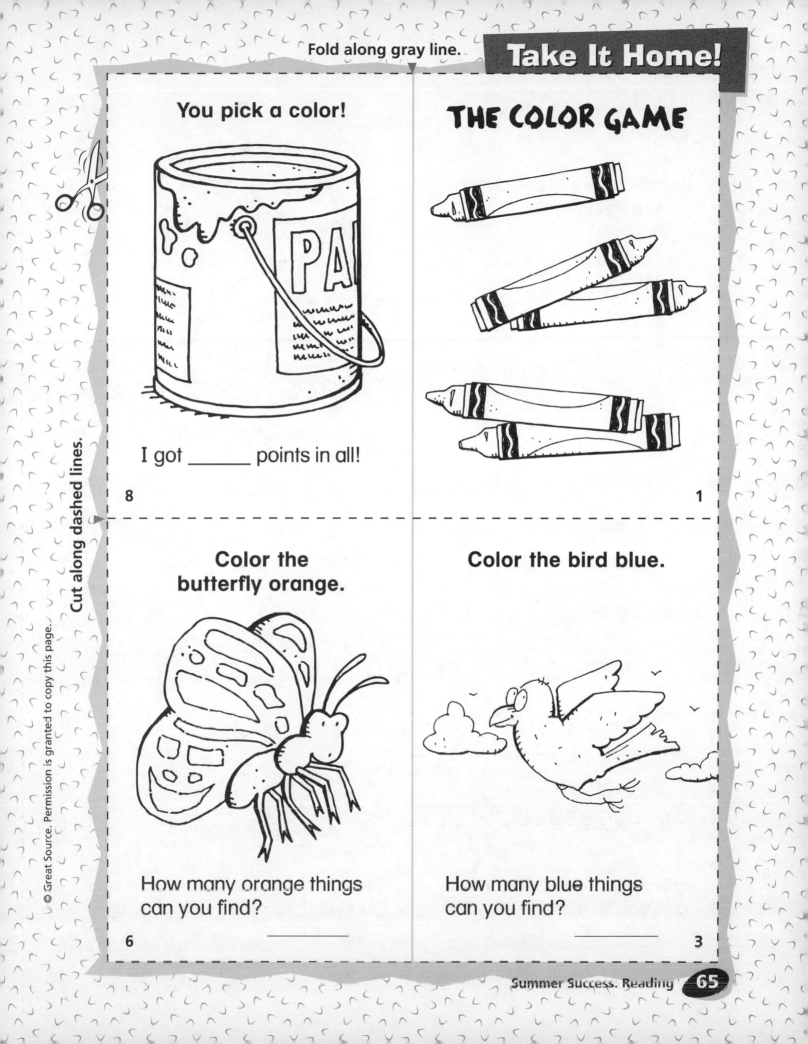

I got _____ points in all!

8

THE COLOR GAME

1

Color the butterfly orange.

How many orange things can you find?

6 _____

Color the bird blue.

How many blue things can you find?

3 _____

Look around your home for different colors.

Match colors to the colors on each page.

Get one point for each match!

2

Color the cat yellow.

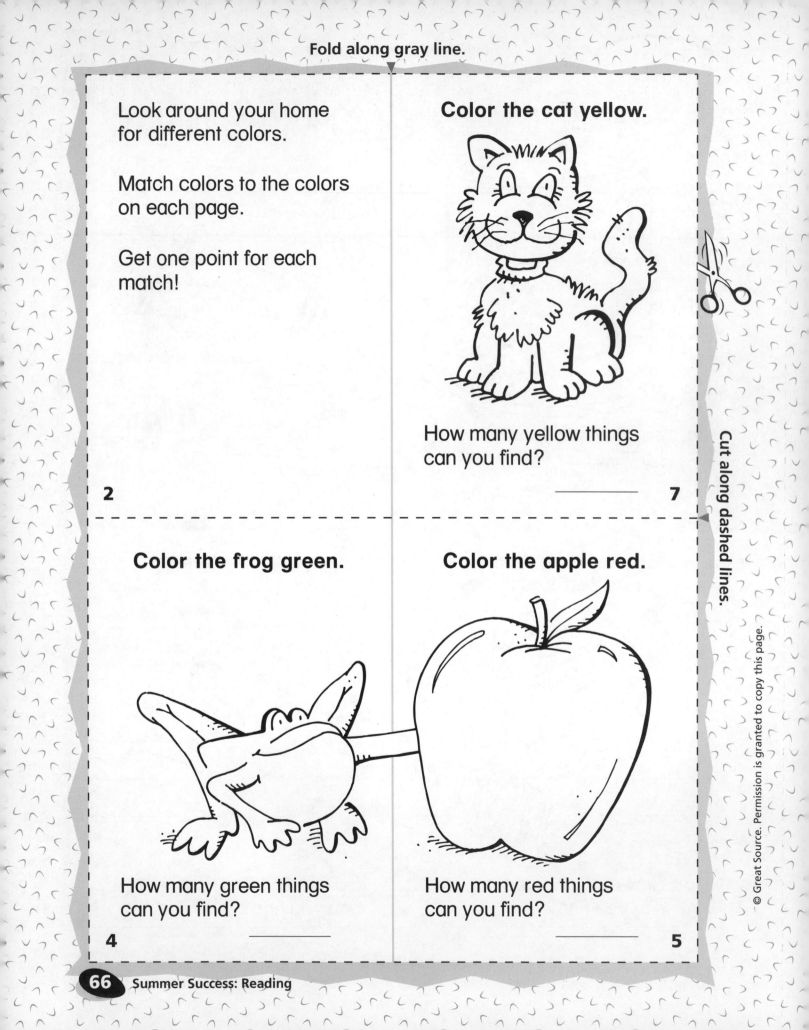

How many yellow things can you find?

_____ **7**

Color the frog green.

How many green things can you find?

4 _____

Color the apple red.

How many red things can you find?

_____ **5**

Week 4 Newsletter

This week we have been reading about colors. We have read a book, some magazine articles, and some poems. Ask your child to tell you about the book that was read aloud and the *Colors* magazine.

The word of the week was *rainbow.* Together, the class listed words that they think of when they hear the word *rainbow.* On another day, the class used the letters in *rainbow* to make words. Then, the class grouped the words by what they had in common— the same beginning sound, the same number of letters, and so on.

Here's what your child has to say about the week:

_____

_____

_____

_____

_____

_____

_____

_____

_____

_____

Word Games

Games are a great way to focus on words and their spellings. No one said learning has to be boring!

Letter by Letter

One person goes through the alphabet, naming an item for each letter. Another person chooses a color for the item. For example, Person One says, "A, apple." Then, Person Two says, "red apple."

Take turns saying the letters and colors. See how fast you can go through the alphabet.

Books to Read Aloud

Here are some books about colors that you may want to share with your child.

***Brown Bear, Brown Bear, What Do You See?* by Bill Martin Jr. (Holt, 1992)**
A classic that is fun to read aloud, especially in pairs. Patterned, rhyming questions ask different animals what they see. Each sees another animal "looking at me."

***Color Dance* by Ann Jonas (Greenwillow, 1989)**
Three dancers with transparent scarves demonstrate how the three primary colors can be combined to achieve a full range of colors.

***A Color of His Own* by Leo Lionni (Dragonfly, 1997)**
Every animal has a color of its own—except for the chameleon. This makes him very sad, until he meets another chameleon who offers to keep him company. Read aloud.

Ants

by Mary Ann Hoberman

I like to watch the ants at work

When I am out at play.

I like to see them run about

And carry crumbs away.

And when I plug an anthill door

To keep them in their den,

I like to see them find a way

To get outside again.

1 Write three words from the poem that end with -ay.

_____

_____

_____

2 Make more words that end with -ay. Add these letters to the beginning of -ay: **d h p**

_____

_____

Making Rhymes

Write the name of the bug in each sentence.

When you finish the sentences, you will have a rhyme.

Read the rhyme out loud to a friend.

Color each picture.

This _____ can jump.

This _____ can crawl.

This _____ can fly.

I like them all!

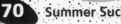

A Butterfly Grows

How does a butterfly become a butterfly?

Number the sentences 1, 2, 3, 4, 5 to show the order.

_____ The caterpillar goes to sleep and grows a hard shell.

_____ A baby bug hatches from an egg.

_____ The baby bug (larva) looks like a little white worm.

_____ The larva becomes a caterpillar.

_____ After many weeks go by, the caterpillar becomes a butterfly.

Here is my picture of a new butterfly.

Story Map

- What happened in the story "Firefly, Firefly"?
- Fill in the story map with words and pictures.
- Retell the story.

Firefly, Firefly

First, _____

_____

_____

Next, _____

_____

_____

Then, _____

_____

_____

Last, _____

_____

_____

Name _____ Date _____

What Did You Learn?

- Read the sentences.
- Put a ✓ in the Yes box if the answer is yes.
- Put a ✓ in the No box if the answer is no.

Ants make spider webs. ☐ **Yes** ☐ **No**

Bees go "buzz, buzz." ☐ **Yes** ☐ **No**

Stink bugs let out a bad smell. ☐ **Yes** ☐ **No**

All bugs are green. ☐ **Yes** ☐ **No**

What else do you know about bugs? _____

_____

_____

_____

_____

Fun with Words

- Make words from the letters in the word <u>spider</u>.
- Write your words in the boxes. Two are done for you.
- You get one point for each word you make.

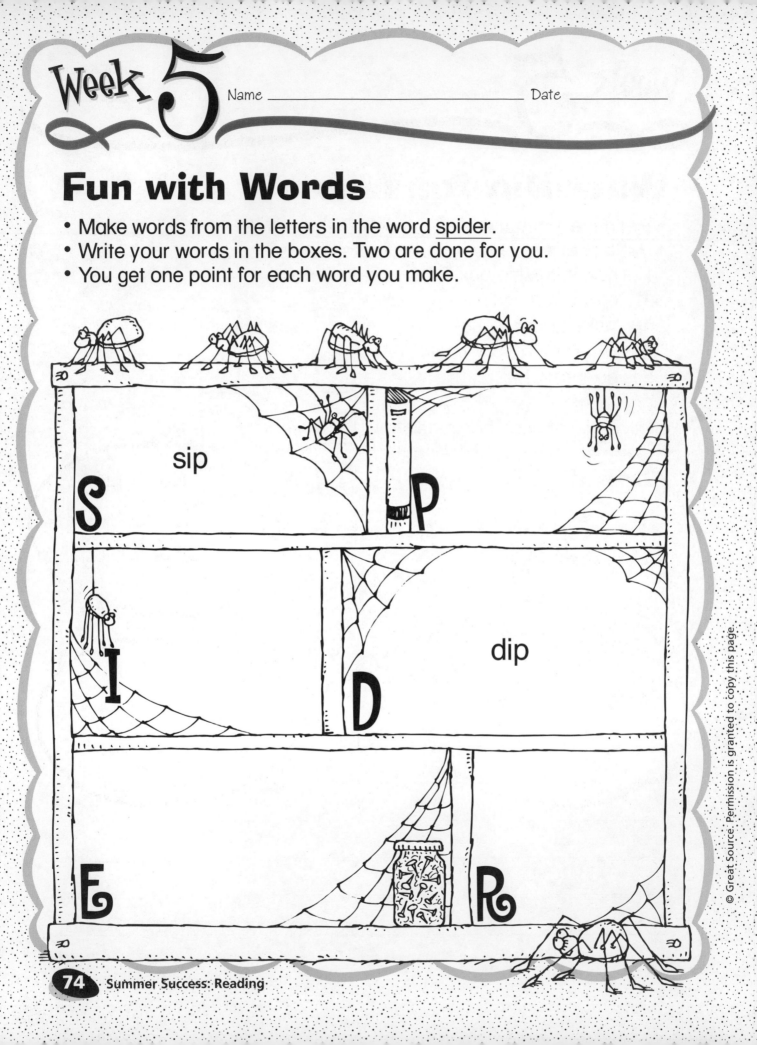

S   sip

P

I

D   dip

E

R

Spider Word Web

- Write a word about a spider web in each circle.
- Write about a spider web.
    how it looks
    how it is made
    what it is for
- Use the words from the web in your writing.

Name _____ Date _____

Retell the Story

- Finish each sentence about the ant and the grasshopper.
- Draw a picture to go with each sentence.

1 At first, Grasshopper and Ant

_____

2 Then Ant had to find food

_____

3 Grasshopper

_____

4 On a snowy day,

_____

5 At the end, Grasshopper told Ant that

_____

Week 5

Name _____ Date _____

Your Own Story

- Plan a story about a busy bee.
- Write and draw your story plans in the boxes.
- Write your story on another sheet of paper.

1 Where does a bee live?

2 How does a bee get around?

3 Where does a bee go?

4 What does a bee make that you can eat?

Self-Evaluation

1 One new thing I tried this week is _____

_____

2 Two new words I learned to read this week are

_____

_____

3 Two new words I learned to write this week are

_____

_____

4 My favorite story or book this week is _____

_____

5 Next week I want to _____

_____

_____

A Walk in the Park

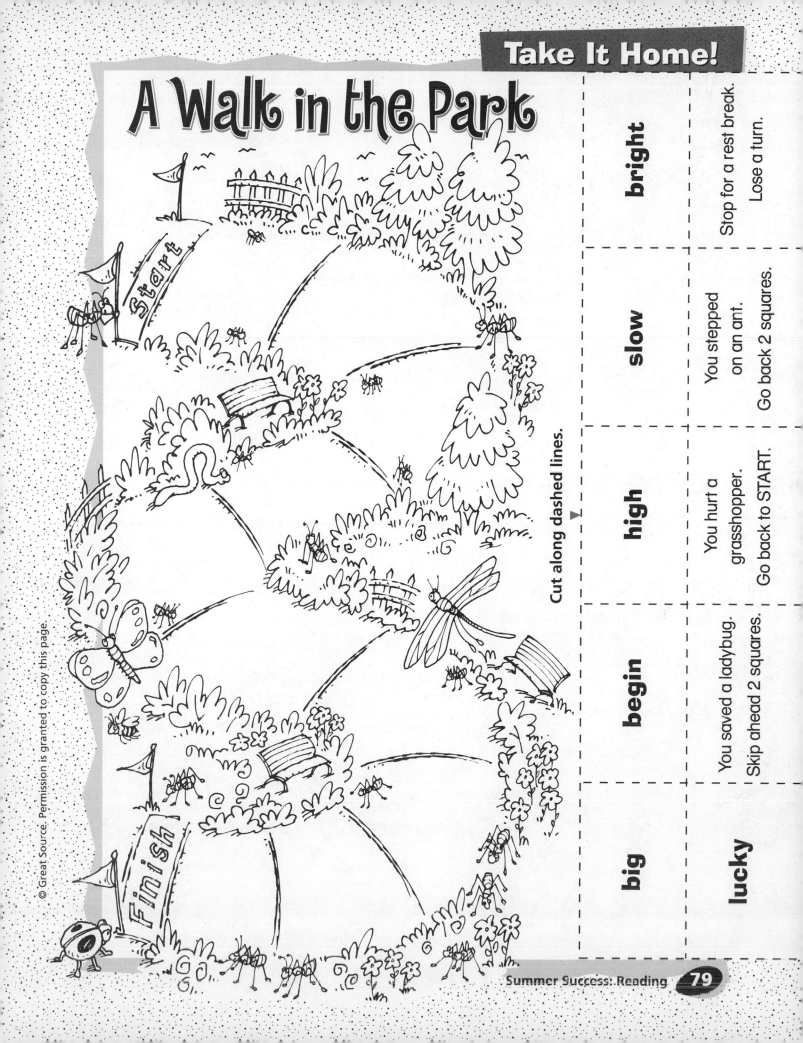

Cut along dashed lines.

bright	slow	high	begin
Stop for a rest break. Lose a turn.	You stepped on an ant. Go back 2 squares.	You hurt a grasshopper. Go back to START.	You saved a ladybug. Skip ahead 2 squares.

big	lucky

How to Play

For 2 or 3 players.
Use coins or paper clips for counters.

DIRECTIONS:

1. Cut out the game cards. Shuffle them.

2. Take turns picking a card.

3. If the card has a word, say another word that has the same meaning or the opposite meaning.

4. If you answer correctly, move ahead one square.

5. If the card has directions, follow them.

6. Put the cards you use in a pile.

What do you do when you finish the pile? Turn the pile over and play some more!

The first player to get through the park and reach FINISH wins.

Week 5 Newsletter

This week we have been reading about bugs. We have read a book, some magazine articles, and some poems. Ask your child to tell you about the book that was read aloud and the *Buggy Bugs* magazine.

The word of the week was *spider*. Together, the class listed words that they think of when they hear the word *spider*. On another day, the class used the letters in *spider* to make words. Then, the words were grouped by what they had in common—the same beginning sound or sounds, the same number of letters, and so on.

Here's what your child has to say about the week:

_____

_____

_____

_____

_____

_____

_____

_____

_____

_____

 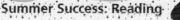

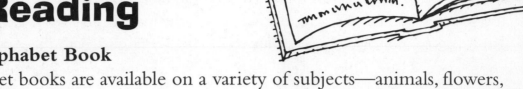

You, Your Child, and Reading

Make an Alphabet Book

Many alphabet books are available on a variety of subjects—animals, flowers, dinosaurs, bugs, and so on. Children of all ages enjoy alphabet books.

Work with your child to make an alphabet book. Decide whether the book will be about one subject or more. Then follow the directions below.

1 Write the 26 letters, one on each page in the top left corner. Make each letter large and clear.

2 Look in old magazines and newspapers for objects to cut out and paste on the appropriate pages. (Put an apple on the A page, a basketball on the B page, and so on.)

3 Label each page with the name of the object or a sentence about the object. Help your child write the words by asking what sounds he or she hears when the words are said slowly.

4 Make a cover.

5 Attach the pages with staples, paper fasteners, or rings.

6 Share the book with an audience!

Dickery Dean

by Dennis Lee

"What's the matter
  With Dickery Dean?
He jumped right into
  The washing machine!"

"Nothing's the matter
  With Dickery Dean—
He dove in dirty,
  And he jumped out clean!"

1 The words <u>Dean</u> and <u>clean</u> rhyme. They sound almost the same. You can make more words that rhyme. Take the <u>cl</u> off <u>clean</u>. Add these letters: **b, l, m.** Write the new words.

_____

_____

_____

2 Draw a picture to go with the poem.

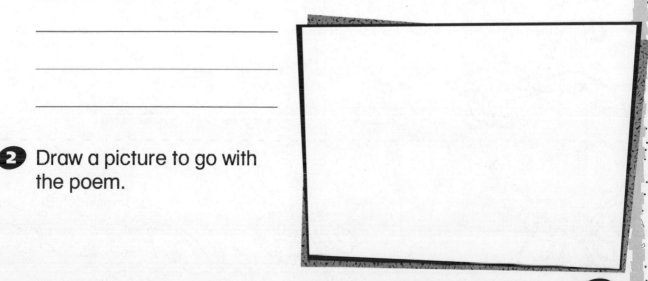

Making Rhymes

- Write a word to make a rhyme.
- Read the rhymes to a friend.

I went to the closet

to get my coat.

I made a mistake

and got my _____ .

I went to the kitchen

to get a plum.

I made a mistake and

got a _____ .

Week 6

Plan a Story

- Make believe you made a funny mistake.
- Plan a story about what you did.
- Draw pictures and write some words.

My Funny Mistake

1 **Where were you?**

2 **What did you do?**

3 **What happened next?**

4 **What happened last?**

Fun with Words

- Make words from the letters in the word <u>laughter</u>.
- Write your words on the chart.
- You get one point for each word you make.

l a u g h t e r

Words with 2 Letters

_____

Words with 3 Letters

_____ _____

_____ _____

_____ _____

_____ _____

_____ _____

Words with 4 Letters

_____ _____

_____ _____

_____ _____

Words with 5 Letters

_____ I got _____ points!

Name _____ Date _____

All About Frogs

- Write four things you learned about frogs.
- Then draw a picture of a frog.

Fact: _____

Fact: _____

Fact: _____

Fact: _____

"The Silly Parade"

- Tell what happened in "The Silly Parade."
- Finish each sentence.
- Then tell the play in your own words.

Billy the rabbit had socks

_____

Gilly the duck had gloves

_____

Milly the monkey had shoes

_____

Willy the wolf had shorts

_____

Cat, Dog, Pig, and Mouse wanted to be silly, too.

They had funny hats _____

Your Silly Parade

- Pretend that you are in a silly parade.
- Draw the mask that you would wear.
- Then write about the silly things you would do.

_____

_____

_____

_____

Knock-Knock Name Jokes

Fill in the blank to make a joke.

Knock, knock.

Who's there?

Kenny.

Kenny who?

Kenny come out _____?

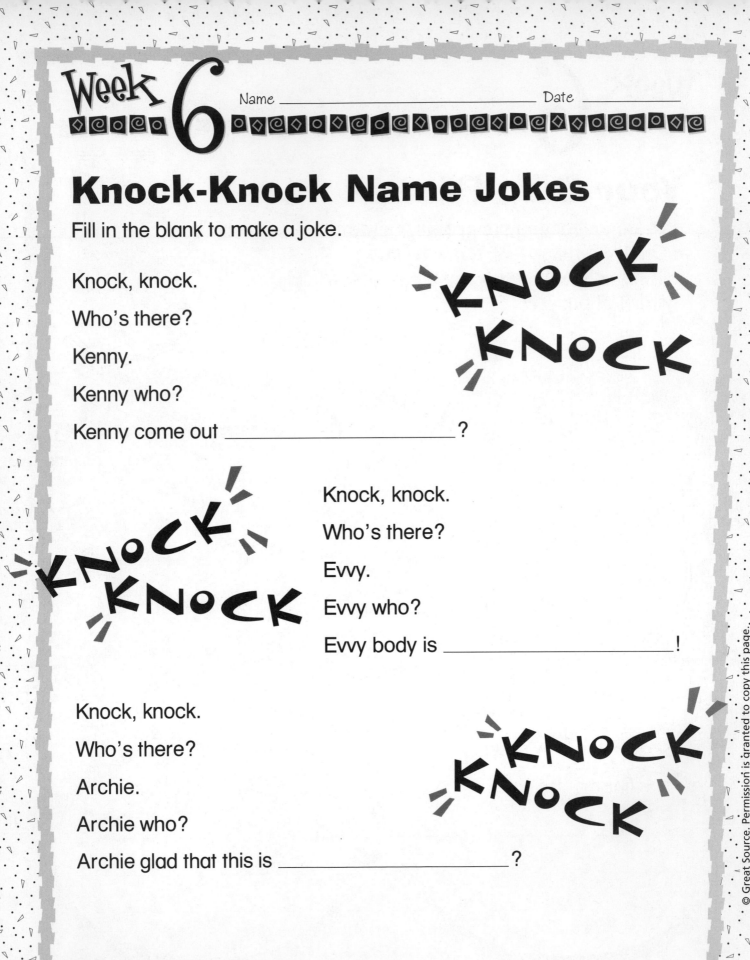

Knock, knock.

Who's there?

Evvy.

Evvy who?

Evvy body is _____!

Knock, knock.

Who's there?

Archie.

Archie who?

Archie glad that this is _____?

Your Own Story

- Plan a story about your Nothing Day.
- Draw your story plans in the web.
- Then write your whole story on another sheet of paper.

First, I did this.

Next, I did this.

My Nothing Day

Then, I did this.

Last, I did this.

Self-Evaluation

1 One new thing I tried this week is _____

_____

_____

_____

2 Two new words I learned to read this week are

_____

_____

3 Two new words I learned to write this week are

_____

_____

4 My favorite story or book this week is _____

_____

5 Next year in school I want to _____

_____

_____

_____

_____

DIRECTIONS:

This is a game called "Around Silly Town."

1 Cut the cards on the lines.

2 Shuffle them and put them in a pile.

3 Player 1 picks a card and makes up a sentence about the picture. Player 2 must spell one of the words that Player 1 said. Then players start a new pile with the used card.

4 What do you do when you finish the cards?

Turn the pile of used cards over and start again!

You get one point for each word spelled correctly.

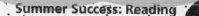

Week 6 Newsletter

This week we have been reading about funny things. We have read a book, some magazine articles, and some poems. Ask your child to tell you about the book that was read aloud and the *Funny Things* magazine.

The word of the week was *laughter*. Together, the class listed words that they think of when they hear the word *laughter*. On another day, the class used the letters in *laughter* to make words. Then, the words were grouped by what they had in common—the same beginning sound, the same number of letters, and so on.

Here's what your child has to say about the week:

_____

_____

_____

_____

_____

_____

_____

_____

You, Your Child, and Reading

Since fresh ideas are always helpful, here are some books that you might read with your child. Laughing is not out of the question, either!

***Abuela* by Arthur Dorros (Dutton, 1991)** In her imagination, Rosalba flies over New York City with her grandmother. The dialogue includes some Spanish, which is all translated into English by Rosalba.

***Arthur's April Fool* by Marc Brown (Little, Brown, 1998)** Arthur is worried about pulling off his magic tricks at the April Fool's Day assembly. Worse, Binky Barnes has promised to pulverize him at the show.

***The Ball Bounced* by Nancy Tafuri (Greenwillow, 1989)** A small boy tosses a ball, sending it through the house and into the backyard. This causes a lot of commotion, especially among the pets.

***Curious George* by H. A. Rey (Houghton Mifflin, 1995)** A monkey is captured and taken from his home in Africa. "Curious George," as he is known, has all sorts of amazing adventures on his way to the United States and his adventures continue after his arrival.

***Green Eggs and Ham* by Dr. Seuss (Random House, 1998)** Sam-I-Am persuades a grouch to try green eggs and ham. Although he at first resists, the grouch finds the dish to be so tasty that he would eat it any place and anytime, under any circumstances. Read aloud.

***I Was Born About 10,000 Years Ago: A Tall Tale* by Steven Kellogg (Morrow, 1996)** The little narrator of this very tall tale has been through it all—from ancient times right up to the present.

***Meet Danitra Brown* by Nikki Grimes (Lothrop, Lee & Shepard, 1994)** A young girl living in an urban city makes up lively rhymes to describe the world around her.

***One Hot Summer Day* by Nina Crews (Greenwillow, 1995)** A little girl has fun getting thoroughly drenched during a sudden rainstorm in New York City.

***Surprises* by Lee Bennett Hopkins (HarperCollins, 1986)** Poems with a humorous take on everyday subjects such as weather, animals, and going places. Poets include Myra Cohn Livingston, Lee Bennett Hopkins, and Gwendolyn Brooks.